First Mental Arithmetic

Teacher's Guide

First Mental Arithmetic

Teacher's Guide

Ann Montague-Smith

Schofield & Sims

Published by **Schofield & Sims Ltd**, Dogley Mill, Fenay Bridge, Huddersfield HD8 0NQ, UK
Telephone 01484 607080
www.schofieldandsims.co.uk

This edition copyright © Schofield & Sims Ltd, 2016
First published in 2013

Author: **Ann Montague-Smith**
Ann Montague-Smith has asserted her moral right under the Copyright, Designs and Patents Act, 1988, to be identified as the author of this work.

British Library Catalogue in Publication Data
A catalogue record for this book is available from the British Library.

Design by **Ledgard Jepson Ltd**
Front cover illustration by **Peter Grundy**
Printed in the UK by **Page Bros (Norwich) Ltd**

ISBN 978 07217 1210 9

CONTENTS

Overview

Schofield & Sims First Mental Arithmetic provides rich and varied practice to meet the requirements of the National Curriculum for primary mathematics.

Comprising six pupil books with accompanying books of answers, as well as this **Teacher's Guide** to cover the whole series, it is designed primarily for Key Stage 1 children – Books 1 to 3 are suitable for Year 1 and Books 4 to 6 for Year 2.

The term 'mental arithmetic' is usually associated with spoken questions that the child works out in their head before providing a verbal or written answer. However, children using **First Mental Arithmetic** read the questions themselves – as in the Key Stage 1 national tests – and may use spare paper to calculate their answers if necessary.

Pupil book structure

The six pupil books are carefully graded. Each book comprises two or three sections divided into separate work sessions. The sessions become more difficult, but the increase in difficulty is gradual. The layout of the work sessions provided in Books 1 to 3 is slightly different from that provided in Books 4 to 6, to suit the age and attention span of the children. Similarly, more questions are provided per session for the older children.

However the basic structure of each session remains constant throughout the series, with the questions arranged in three parts, as follows:

- **Part A**: questions where the use of language is kept to a minimum, and symbols and numbers are used

- **Part B**: questions where mathematical language is used

- **Part C**: written questions that involve one- or two-step problem solving.

Additional Check-up Tests focus on particular areas that children might find difficult.

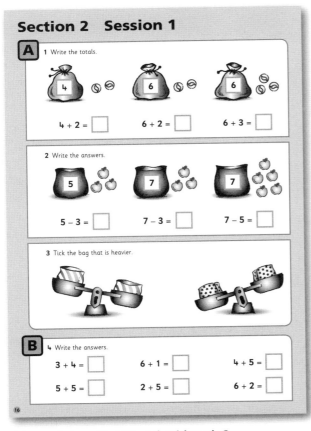

This page is from **First Mental Arithmetic 2**.

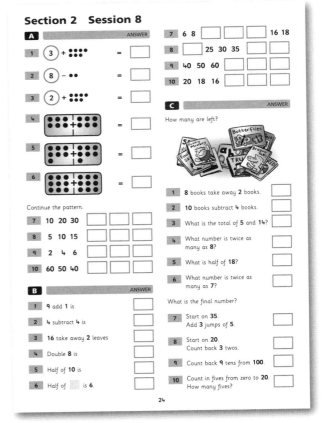

This page is from **First Mental Arithmetic 4**.

Books 1 to 3

Books 1 to 3 are designed primarily for children in Year 1, with each providing enough work for one term. Each of these books is divided into two sections – one for each half-term. A whole double-page spread is given to each session. The layout is spacious and includes illustrations and a number line on every spread.

Each session is divided into three parts, A, B and C, as described on page 6, generally with three questions per part – totalling nine questions per spread.

Books 4 to 6

Books 4 to 6 are designed primarily for children in Year 2. Each of these books provides a year's worth of work and is divided into three sections – one for each term. Within each section are at least ten work sessions (12 in Book 6). One page is given to each session.

Again, each session is divided into three parts, A, B and C, as described above. In these three books, however, there are 10 questions per part – totalling 30 questions per page.

The layout, structure and content of the sessions in Books 4 to 6 is very similar to that of the tests provided in **Mental Arithmetic**, providing a helpful bridge to the Key Stage 2 series.

Three Achievement Charts are provided – one for each section of the book – and these enable the children to monitor their own progress. After each session has been marked, encourage the children to colour in the relevant box for each question that they have answered correctly.

Just Facts questions help to secure the children's knowledge of addition, subtraction, multiplication and division facts.

Teacher's Guide

This **Teacher's Guide** introduces the series and outlines ways to use the books on a day-to-day basis. It contains two sets of resources.

- **Assessment Resources** include tests to help you to select the most appropriate pupil book for each child, as well as a Group Record Sheet and diagnostic support for children who are struggling to meet age-related expectations. This resource set also features contents pages from each of the six pupil books. These will show you at a glance the areas of maths that are covered in each book.

- **General Resources** provide a range of copymasters to help you develop the children's maths skills. These may be copied as handouts or enlarged and used as posters.

A full list of **First Mental Arithmetic** books is provided at the back of this guide.

Purpose

Schofield & Sims First Mental Arithmetic is intended for use alongside your existing maths lessons. It gives children the opportunity to develop their understanding of mathematical concepts already taught in class by providing carefully differentiated questions in the volume necessary for intensive and regular use.

It is vital that you introduce new concepts and teach these thoroughly before the children meet them in the **First Mental Arithmetic** books. This will give them the chance to do well, showing you what they know, as well as what they may have forgotten. Targeted questions focus on the different areas of the curriculum, providing structured, rigorous practice of key concepts, and highlighting those areas where children need further help.

First Mental Arithmetic also reinforces and develops children's maths vocabulary. Each pupil book includes a 'Language of Maths' glossary and all six of these are reproduced in the **General Resources** section of this **Teacher's Guide**.

First Mental Arithmetic and the National Curriculum

By providing rich and varied maths practice and on-going formative assessment, **First Mental Arithmetic** meets the requirements of the National Curriculum, enabling children to consolidate their essential maths skills and develop a deeper understanding of the topics covered. The range of topics per session encourages children to think mathematically and apply all that they have learnt when answering each question, as well as helping them to improve their mental fluency.

Children should demonstrate mastery of the curriculum content for their year group before they are allowed to move on to a later book in the series. The increase in difficulty within each book will challenge and extend more able children, providing comprehensive practice and highlighting any gaps in their understanding.

To assist you in choosing the right book for each child or class, two Entry Tests are provided (see below for more information).

Using First Mental Arithmetic

First Mental Arithmetic may be used in many different ways, including:

- individual work, with children who are confident with the maths concepts covered

- maths recovery, to assess new or struggling children and to improve mental fluency

- paired work, allowing children who lack confidence in some concepts to discuss the questions and think of possible ways to answer them

- group or whole-class work, working through a set of questions with a group of children after they have answered them

- homework, with parents and carers encouraging children to explain their working methods.

Selecting the right book for your class

First Mental Arithmetic makes it easy for you to provide work for different abilities within a class or group, using two Entry Tests to help you select the right book for each child or class. Children working significantly above or below age-related expectations may work on the book best suited to their needs. This means that all children will be working at their own pace, giving you the time to support those who need your help – including those with special educational needs.

Two **First Mental Arithmetic** Entry Tests are provided:

- Entry Test A is suitable for Year 1 and covers **First Mental Arithmetic 1** to **3**

- Entry Test B is suitable for Year 2 and covers **First Mental Arithmetic 4** to **6**.

Both Entry Tests are designed to help you to establish the starting point for each child. You may wish to test all the class or, if you are already using the series, only those whose competency in mathematics you are unsure of. **First Mental Arithmetic** is designed to consolidate children's understanding of concepts already taught.

Administering the Entry Tests

Before administering the Entry Tests, ensure that you have a sharp pencil, a photocopy of the appropriate test and some spare paper for each child.

Explain to the child or the class the following points:

- the purpose of the test is to make sure that the maths work they do on a daily basis is at a suitable level – not too easy or too difficult for them

- only the individual and the teacher will know the results of the test

- the test is not timed but is likely to take about an hour

- the questions are arranged to become increasingly difficult as they work through the test

- there will come a point when they are unable to answer any more questions – and at this point they may read quietly so as not to disturb others who are still working

- they should try to do their best.

You may then distribute the Entry Test and tell the children to start.

Marking the Entry Tests

Use the Entry Test marking keys to mark the test. One mark is given for each correct answer. Where a question has two parts, give half a mark for each part.

When everyone's test is marked, note the results on a copy of the Group Record Sheet. The table below indicates which **First Mental Arithmetic** book will be most suitable for each child, based on their Entry Test score.

Entry Test	Entry Test total score	Schofield & Sims First Mental Arithmetic book
Entry Test A	0–15	First Mental Arithmetic 1
	16–30	First Mental Arithmetic 2
	31–45	First Mental Arithmetic 3
Entry Test B	0–15	First Mental Arithmetic 4
	16–30	First Mental Arithmetic 5
	31–45	First Mental Arithmetic 6

Daily First Mental Arithmetic sessions

Try to make time each day when the children work through part of a session. Some schools find that 10 to 20 minutes' work is best and you may find this easiest to fit in as an early morning starter activity at the beginning of the day.

When you first introduce the books, tell the children that:

- they should do their best to answer the questions

- they can refer to you or to another adult if they need some guidance

- they can talk to a friend to discuss any question that they find difficult

- if a question is causing difficulty they can miss it out.

Group marking sessions

Many teachers organise weekly marking sessions in which all the questions completed during the week are marked together, as follows:

- as you prepare for the session, make sure that you have the relevant answer book

- work through the questions, reading each one out in turn to ensure that everyone is focused and understands the vocabulary

- invite one child to answer the question and to explain how they worked out the answer

- clearly explain to the children whether this answer is correct or not, and tell the children to mark their own answers accordingly

- other children may have used a different method from the one demonstrated: discuss which method is the most efficient and why

- if a child gives the wrong answer, model the correct answer on the board.

Diagnostic Checks

A two-page Diagnostic Check, covering key concepts, is provided for each book: see the **Assessment Resources** section of this **Teacher's Guide**. Use the checks with any individuals or groups of children who have struggled with the maths concepts in the **First Mental Arithmetic** book that they are currently using.

The questions in each Diagnostic Check are grouped by topic. The relevant marking key provides corrective activities for each topic, in the form of activity prompts. These recommend ways in which you or another adult can help the child with a concept that they may not have understood. After using the prompt, give further examples of the concept for the child to think through. Begin with simple items and move to more complex ones. Many other activities may be developed from these initial ideas. Use the activities diagnostically to assess the child's understanding of the concept.

Some of the activities suggest that, at first, children use their fingers to keep track of the mental count. Over time, encourage the children to visualise the number line instead.

Monitoring progress and rewarding achievement

The **First Mental Arithmetic** pupil books provide a permanent record of work, and the children are encouraged both to monitor their own progress and to take pride in the development of their maths skills.

If you wish to acknowledge and reward those children whose achievements – at whatever level – are especially significant, you may download blank editable certificates from the **Free downloads** section of the Schofield & Sims website (details at the back of this guide). These certificates are also an effective way to communicate children's achievements to their parents and carers.

Schofield & Sims First Mental Arithmetic

Assessment Resources

Use these resources to help you decide which **First Mental Arithmetic** book a child or class should begin with.

Entry Tests A and B, the Group Record Sheet and all the Diagnostic Checks may be photocopied after purchase for use within your school or institution only.

Contents

Schofield & Sims First Mental Arithmetic 1

Contents

Schofield & Sims First Mental Arithmetic 2

Contents

Schofield & Sims First Mental Arithmetic 3

Contents

Schofield & Sims First Mental Arithmetic 4

Contents

Schofield & Sims First Mental Arithmetic 5

Contents

Schofield & Sims First Mental Arithmetic 6

Schofield & Sims First Mental Arithmetic
Entry Test A

Name:		
Class:		Date:

ANSWER

1 Count the dots.

2 Write these numbers in order.

10   4   7

3 **1** more than **8** is

4 **1** less than **10** is

5 7 + 3 =

6 4 + = 10

7 Write the missing numbers.

5   6   7

8 Write the missing numbers.

0   5 **20**

9 4 + 6 =

10 7 + = 9

ANSWER

11 8 − 3 =

12 7 − = 4

13 Draw a triangle.

14 Draw a line longer than this line.

Draw a line shorter than the printed line above.

15 Here are some vegetables.

Carrots   Sprouts   Leeks

(a) How many more carrots than leeks are there?   (a)

(b) How many fewer sprouts than leeks are there?   (b)

ANSWER

ANSWER

16 Count the spots.

17 Write these numbers in order.

14   17   11

18 Write the number.

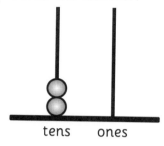

tens   ones

19 **10 + 4 =**

20 **15 − 1 =**

21 **50** add **10** equals

22 **40** subtract **10** leaves

23 What is **9** add **9**?

24 Continue the pattern.

0   10   20

25 Use the pictures to help you.

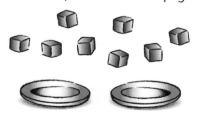

8 shared by **2** is

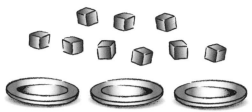

26 **9** shared by **3** is

27 Draw the hands to show the time.

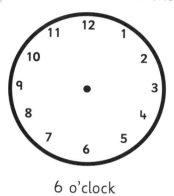

6 o'clock

28 Tick the heavier one.

29 Freya needs to go straight home.
Draw a line to show which path
she should choose.

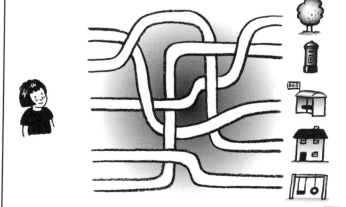

ANSWER

ANSWER

30 Tick the thing that can turn.

31 Write all the missing numbers.

13 ▮ ▮ ▮ ▮ **18**

32 Show **15** on this abacus.

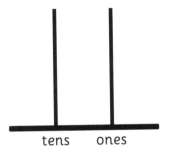

tens   ones

33 **1** more than **14** is

34 **1** less than **18** is

35 **9 + 4 =**

36 **7** and **5** equals

37 **3** more than **6** is

38 The difference between **8** and **2** is

39 I spend **6p**. What is my change from **20p**?

p

40 Double **9** is

41 (a) **12** shared by **3** is

(a)

(b) **12** shared by **2** is

(b)

42 Draw the hands to show half past **3**.

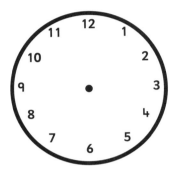

43 Put a tick on the right-hand top corner of this square.

Now draw a line to cut the square in half.

44 Write the numbers into the space where they belong.

1 2 3 4 5 6 7 8 9 10

An even number	An odd number

45 How many blocks long is the string?

blocks

Entry Test A marking key

1   15

2   4   7   10

3   9

4   9

5   10

6   6

7   8   9   10

8   10   15

9   10

10   2

11   5

12   3

13   Drawing of a triangle

14   First one line that is longer, then one shorter than the given line

15   (a) 3   (b) 1

16   18

17   11   14   17

18   20

19   14

20   14

21   60

22   30

23   18

24   30   40

25   4

26   3

27   Hands to show 6 o'clock

28   Left-hand side of balance ticked

29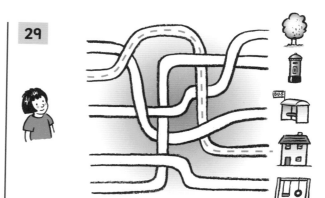

30   Scissors (they make a turning action as they open and close) ticked

31   14   15   16   17

32

tens   ones

33   15

34   17

35   13

36   12

37   9

38   6

39   14p

40   18

41   (a) 4   (b) 6

42   Hands on clock face to show 3.30

43   Tick must be placed on or near top right-hand corner

Line can be horizontal, vertical or diagonal

44

An even number	An odd number
2 4 6 8 10	1 3 5 7 9

The numbers may be shown in any order.

45   6 blocks

Schofield & Sims First Mental Arithmetic
Entry Test B

| Name: | |
| Class: | Date: |

ANSWER

1 Write eighteen as a number.

2 Draw beads for **23**.

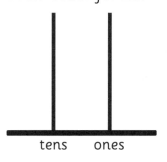

tens   ones

3 How many tens in **47**?   ___ tens

4 How many ones in **53**?   ___ ones

5 **5 + 3 =**

6   **20p** – **4p**   ___ p

7 Write the number that is **1** more than **4** tens and **6** ones.

Write **<** or **>** to make the number sentences true.

8 **29** ▮ **31**

9 **92** ▮ **13**

10 What number is half of **16**?

ANSWER

11 **6 × 2 =**

12 **40 ÷ 5 =**

13 Draw hands to show ten past **9**.

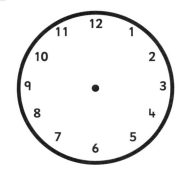

14 Put an arrow at **38cm**.

30cm   40cm

15 Sketch a pentagon.

16 Write the next odd number after **143**.

17 What is double **14**?

18 ▨ − 6 = 48

ANSWER
[   ]

19 How much change from **20p** for a lolly at **9p** and a chew for **6p**?

[   ] p

20 8 + ▨ = 20

[   ]

21 ▨ multiplied by **2** is **18**.

[   ]

22 How much is five **5p** coins?

[   ] p

23 **30** shared by **5** is

[   ]

24 A quarter of **12** is

[   ]

25 Three-quarters of **12** is

[   ]

26 The product of **10** and **10** is

[   ]

27 Write the name of this shape.

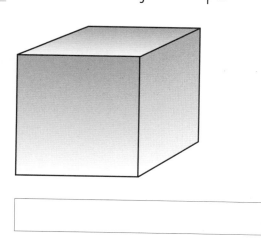

[   ]

28 Write the numbers from **1** to **20** onto the diagram.

ANSWER

	Even	Not even
Numbers greater than **9**		
Numbers not greater than **9**		

[ ]

29 Peter has **14** metres of rope. He cuts the rope in half. How long is each piece?

[   ] m

30 Look at the two clocks.

How far has the minute hand turned? Write whole, half or quarter turn.

[   ]

ANSWER

ANSWER

31 Write four hundred and ninety-two in digits.

42 Write the name of this shape.

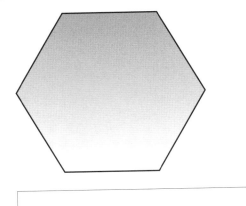

32 93 – 50 =

33 66 + ▢ = 96

34 Subtract **70g** from **97g**. g

35 Which is larger, **58** or **85**?

43 How many right angles are there in the shape above?

36 42 – ▢ = 37

37 35 ÷ 5 =

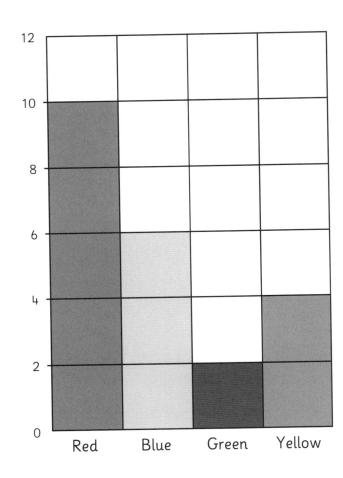

38 ▢ + 60 = 100

39 8 × ▢ = 16

40 Divide **14** by **2**.

41 There are **16** squares of chocolate.

How many squares in three-quarters of the chocolate?

squares

44 Which is the most popular colour?

45 How many more did blue score than green?

Entry Test B marking key

1 18

2

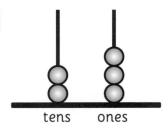

tens   ones

3 4 tens

4 3 ones

5 8

6 16p

7 47

8 <

9 >

10 8

11 12

12 8

13 Hands to show ten past 9

14

30cm   40cm

15 Sketch of a pentagon

16 145

17 28

18 54

19 5p

20 12

21 9

22 25p

23 6

24 3

25 9

26 100

27 Cube

28

	Even	Not even
Numbers greater than 9	10 12 14 16 18 20	11 13 15 17 19
Numbers not greater than 9	2 4 6 8	1 3 5 7 9

The numbers may be shown in any order.

29 7m

30 Quarter turn

31 492

32 43

33 30

34 27g

35 85

36 5

37 7

38 40

39 2

40 7

41 12 squares

42 Hexagon

43 0 or None

44 Red

45 4

Entry Test
Group Record Sheet

Schofield & Sims First Mental Arithmetic

Class	Teacher's name	Date of test

Child's name	Entry test total score	Schofield & Sims First Mental Arithmetic book					
		1	2	3	4	5	6
Total number of books required:							

Diagnostic Check: First Mental Arithmetic 1

Name:

Class:

Date:

ANSWER

1 Write how many dots.

2 Write these numbers in order.

9　6　10

3 Write the number that is **1** more than **7**.

4 Write the number that is **1** less than **8**.

Write the answers.

5 $2 + 2 =$

6 **3** and **2** is

7 **5** take away **2** leaves

8 **4** take away **4** leaves

9 **6** add **4** equals

10 $9 + 1 =$

ANSWER

11 **3** add **7** makes

12 **5** and ▢ equals **10**.

13 Join the shapes to their label.

Square

Rectangle

Triangle

Circle

14 Draw **13** dots.

15 Write the missing numbers.

▢　**6**　**7**　▢　▢　**10**

ANSWER

ANSWER

16 Draw a line shorter than this line.

17 Draw a line longer than this line.

Marbles

23 Harry has **8** marbles.
He gives half of his
marbles to Eshe.
How many marbles
does Eshe have?

18 Write the missing numbers.

Colour of house doors

Blue

Red

Brown

Black

24 Today is Thursday.
What day will it be tomorrow?

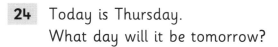

25 Today is Saturday.
What day was it yesterday?

19 **3 + 3 =**

20 What is double **4**?

Write the answers.

26 **6 + 3 =**

21 What is half of **10**?

27 **8 − 6 =**

28 **3 + 4 =**

29 **9 − 5 =**

22 Ava has **6** toffees.
She eats **3** toffees.
How many toffees
does Ava have now?

30 Continue the pattern.

5   10   15

Diagnostic Check: First Mental Arithmetic 2

Name:	
Class:	Date:

ANSWER

Count the spots. Write how many.

1

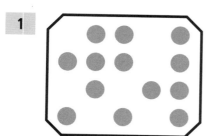

2

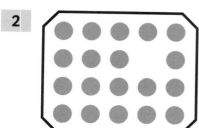

3 Write these numbers in order.

14   9   15   12

4 Write the number shown on this abacus.

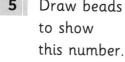

tens   ones

5 Draw beads to show this number.

1	**9**

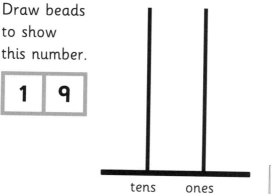

tens   ones

ANSWER

6   **10 + 5 =**

7   **6** take away **4** leaves

8   Rakesh has **8** sweets. He gives **4** sweets to Noah. How many sweets does Rakesh have now?

9   Hannah has **5** pencils and Max has **4** pencils. How many pencils is that altogether?

10   **17 + ▢ = 18**

11   **19 – 1 =**

12   **20 + ▢ = 30**

13   **▢ – 10 = 30**

Start at zero.

14   Make **4** jumps of **2**.

15   Make **2** jumps of **5**.

16   Make **4** jumps of **10**.

17   Make **6** jumps of **5**.

ANSWER

ANSWER

26 Draw a cup. Draw a line to show that it is full of water.

18 **10** shared by **2** is

19 **10** shared by **5** is

20 **10** shared by **10** is

27 Draw the shapes.

Square   Triangle

Circle   Rectangle

21 Ethan has **8** grapes. He shares the grapes equally with Archie. How many grapes does Archie have?

22 Write the time.

28 Draw these shapes.

3 circles

2 rectangles

23 Draw the hands to show the time.

4 o'clock

29 Draw a chair.
Draw a book on the chair.

24 Shula leaves home at **4** o'clock. She gets to the airport at **7** o'clock. How long does her journey take?

hours

25 Draw a pencil. Draw a longer pencil and put a tick on it.

30 Look at the chair you have drawn. Now draw a ball under the chair.

Diagnostic Check: First Mental Arithmetic 3

Name:

Class:

Date:

ANSWER

1 Write the missing numbers.

12 13 ▓ ▓ 16 ▓

2 Poppy has a bag of **10** toffees and **6** more. Write how many toffees Poppy has.

3 1 more than **19** is

4 10 less than **40** is

5 3 + ▓ = 10

6 Erin has **£4** and Sovanna has **£5**. How much money is that in total?
£

7 8 subtract **5** is

8 There are **14** sheep in the field. The farmer moves **3** sheep to the barn. How many sheep are there in the field now?

9 Double **6** is

10 There are **8** flowers in the red vase and **8** flowers in the blue vase. How many flowers is that altogether?

ANSWER

11 $5 + 5 + 5 + 5 =$

12 Tom hops in **2s** from **0** along the number track. He makes **6** hops. What number does he land on?

13 Sam has four **10p** pieces. How much money is that in total?
p

14 Hadiya has four **5p** coins. How much money does Hadiya have?
p

15 15 shared by **5** is

16 There are **14** apples in the box. Share these equally between **2** bowls. How many apples go into each bowl?

17 **50** counters are shared equally between **10** children. How many counters does each child have?

18 What is half of **6**?

19 What is half of **10**?

20 What is a quarter of **8**?

ANSWER

21 Put a tick below the picture that belongs in the shaded box.

22 Draw the other half of the picture.

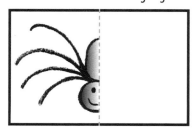

23 Sort these numbers.

12 15 30 18 6 10 9 5

A multiple of **5**	Not a multiple of **5**

24 Join the shapes to where they fit in the diagram.

Has **4** sides	Does not have **4** sides

25 Tick the clocks that show half past times.

ANSWER

26 Draw the hands to show the time.

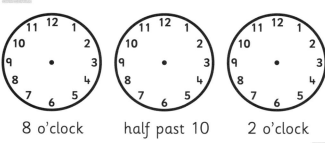

8 o'clock   half past 10   2 o'clock

27 Adam goes out to play at **9** o'clock. He comes back into his house at **11** o'clock. How long has he been playing outside?

hours

28 Draw a chair. Now draw a cat on the chair.

29 Look at your drawing of a chair and a cat. Now draw a mouse underneath the chair.

30 Draw something that turns.

Diagnostic Check: First Mental Arithmetic 4

Name:

Class: Date:

1 Write nineteen as a number.   ANSWER

2 Write the missing numbers.

20   **40**   **60**

3 Write the odd number just before **50**.

4 Here are some numbers.

44   56   77

Write the odd number in words.

Write the numbers that fit with the number you are given.

5 Up to **50**

45 <

6 Between **60** and **70**

67 >

7 6 + 7 + 4 =

8 8 + 4 + 2 =

9 3 + 5 + 7 =

10 **56 + 5 =**   ANSWER

11 **72 − 4 =**

12 Lukas has **56p**. He spends **9p**. How much money does he have left?   p

13 A bag of marshmallows costs **36p**. How much change would there be from **50p**?   p

14 Double **4** is

15 Half of **16** is

16 **2kg** of carrots cost **18p**. How much does **1kg** of carrots cost?   p

17 **9 × 2 =**

18 **8 × 5 =**

19 **14 ÷ 2 =**

20 What is **35** shared between **5**?

21 Half of **16** is

ANSWER

22 A quarter of **16** is

23 Three-quarters of **16** is

24 What length does the arrow show?

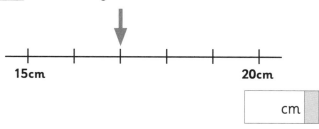

cm

25 Put an arrow at **46cm**.

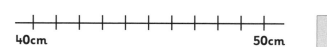

Draw hands to show these times.

26

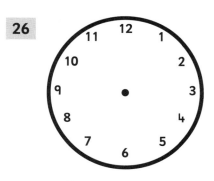

Quarter past four

27

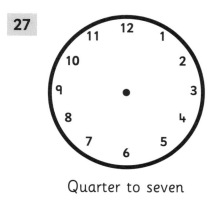

Quarter to seven

ANSWER

28 Sketch each shape under its name.

Triangle

Rectangle

Pentagon

29 Join the 3-D shapes to their names.

Cone

Pyramid

Sphere

30 Draw a circle.

Diagnostic Check: First Mental Arithmetic 5

Name:

Class: | Date:

ANSWER

1 Write **492** in words.

2 Fill in the gaps.

8 ☐ is the same as

☐ tens and **3** ones.

3 Sort these numbers onto the sorting diagram.

81 94 36 82 75
10 49 37

Is odd	Is not odd

4 Will the answer to **36 + 27** be odd or even?

5 Double **16** is

6 Double **19** is

7 The shopkeeper has seven **2p** coins and fourteen **1p** coins in the till. How much money is that in total?   p

8 46 + ☐ = 50

ANSWER

9 9 + ☐ = 20

Write the change from **20p**.

10 Spend **12p**.   p

11 Spend **17p**.   p

12 9 × 5 =

13 6 × ☐ = 60

14 Share **45** peaches between **5** children. How many does each child receive?

15 ☐ divided by **2** equals **7**.

16 Emma has **6** boxes of pencils. Each box has **5** pencils in it. How many pencils is that altogether?

17 Shade three-quarters of this shape.

ANSWER

18 What is $\frac{1}{2}$ of **24**?

19 What is $\frac{1}{4}$ of **24**?

20 Join the shapes to their names.

 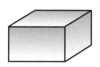

Cuboid   Cone   Cube

21 Draw a line of symmetry.

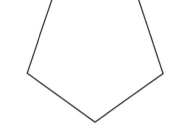

22 Write the number **41** on this scale.

23 Write the number **46** on this scale.

Draw the hands on the clocks to show the times.

24 Ten past three

25 Twenty to six

ANSWER

26 Jake leaves home at five to nine and walks to the shops.
He gets home again at ten past nine.
How long does he take?

27 How many minutes in three-quarters of an hour?

minutes

Write whole, half or quarter turn as your answer.

28 Jamie turns to look at the door.
How far has he turned?

29 Jamie faces front.
He turns to face the clock.
How far has he turned?

30 From looking at the clock Jamie turns to face the chair.
How far has he turned?

Diagnostic Check: First Mental Arithmetic 6

Name:

Class: Date:

ANSWER

1 Write nine hundred and ninety-nine in digits.

2 Write **64** on this number line.

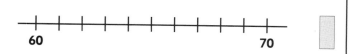

60   70

Use < or > to make these number sentences true.

3 63 ▮ 36

4 89 ▮ 98

5 47 + 50 =

6 ▮ + 18 = 20

7 Write the total of **52cm** and **30cm**.

cm

8 What is the difference between **90g** and **75g**?

g

9 8 × 2 =

10 4 × 5 =

11 ▮ × 10 = 60

ANSWER

Marbles

12 **40** marbles shared between **5** is

Biscuits

13 **50** biscuits packed in **10s**. How many packs?

14 11 + ▮ = 20

15 30 + ▮ = 100

There are **30** plums and **17** apples in the basket.

16 How many is half of the plums?

17 How many is double the number of apples?

ANSWER

ANSWER

18 How many squares are half?

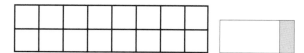

19 What is three-quarters of **16**?

Write the time for these clocks.

20

21

22 How many minutes are there between **6.45** and **7.15**?

minutes

Write where the arrow points.

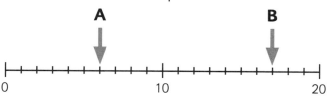

23 A

24 B

Write the name of the **3-D** shape.

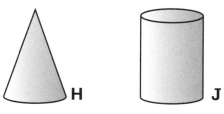

25 H

26 J

27 Sketch a triangle with a right angle.

28 Sketch a circle.

How many right angles inside these shapes?

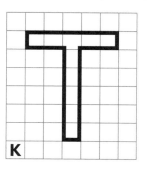

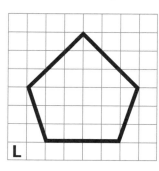

29 K

30 L

Diagnostic Check marking key: First Mental Arithmetic 1

Below each set of answers you will find **Activity prompts** for helping children to overcome difficulties. Use these activities diagnostically so that you can assess when children understand the concept.

Counting quantities to 10

1 9

> **Activity prompt:** Provide practical experience of counting given quantities of counters. Check that children coordinate the touch of the counter and saying the number and that each counter is counted just once. When children are confident, provide experience of counting out a specific amount.

Ordering numbers

2 6 9 10

> **Activity prompt:** Use 'Numeral cards from 0 to 9'. Ask children to order the cards. Then repeat with randomly chosen cards, three at a time.

1 more/less than

3 8   **4** 7

> **Activity prompt:** Use 'Number lines from 0 to 20' to help children to see the order of the numbers. Ask them to count on 1 more/1 less from given numbers. Then ask them to do this mentally.

Addition and subtraction to 5

5 4   **6** 5   **7** 3   **8** 0

> **Activity prompt:** Encourage children to count on or back mentally to find the answer. At first they may use their fingers. For example: *2 add 2: Start at 2, then count on: 3, 4. So 2 add 2 is 4.*

Totals of 10

9 10   **10** 10   **11** 10   **12** 5

> **Activity prompt:** Encourage counting on to find the answer. For example: *6 add 4: Start at 6 and count on: 7, 8, 9, 10. So 6 add 4 makes 10.*

Common 2-D shapes

13

Square
Rectangle
Triangle
Circle

> **Activity prompt:** Provide shape tiles and labels with the names written on. Read the labels together. Encourage children to sort the tiles into sets, all the circles together and so on. Then ask them to place the labels by the relevant shape tiles.

Counting up to 15 objects

14 Count to check that there are 13 dots.

> **Activity prompt:** Provide counters and suggest children put out 13 counters, as for this question.

Counting patterns of 1s

15 5 8 9

> **Activity prompt:** Count orally. Count along a number line, such as 'Number lines from 0 to 20'. Ask children to order 'Numeral cards from 0 to 9'. Repeat with a set of cards, such as 3, 4, 5, 6, shuffled.

Longer and shorter

16 Check that the drawn line is shorter than the printed line.

17 Check that the line drawn is longer than the printed line.

> **Activity prompt:** Provide practical examples of making comparisons of length and ask children to say each time, for example: *The pencil is shorter than the ruler. The ruler is longer than the pencil.*

Simple pictograms

18 Blue 6, Red 3, Brown 4, Black 5

> **Activity prompt:** Ask children to collect some evidence, such as how many blue, green and yellow pencils there are in a box. Then ask them to make their own simple pictogram of their results, perhaps using computer software.

Doubles and halves

19 6   **20** 8   **21** 5   **22** 3   **23** 4

> **Activity prompt:** Provide interlocking cubes. Ask children to count out, say, 3, then another 3, and to determine what the double of 3 is. Then challenge them to count on from 3 mentally to find the double. For halves, ask them to count, say, 10 cubes, then find the half by breaking the tower of cubes to make two equal towers. Point out that double 5 is 10, and half of 10 is 5, so if they know the double they also can work out mentally the half.

Days of the week

24 Friday   **25** Friday

> **Activity prompt:** Each day ask the children to say what day it is, what day yesterday was, and what day tomorrow is. Display 'Days of the week' so that the children have a reference for the order and spelling of the days.

Addition and subtraction to 10

26 9   **27** 2   **28** 7   **29** 4

> **Activity prompt:** Encourage mental calculations, with children counting on from the larger number for addition. They can also count up from the smaller to the larger number to find the difference for subtraction.

Counting in 5s

30 20

> **Activity prompt:** Count from zero in 5s to 20 as a class activity. Provide numeral cards 0, 5, 10, 15, 20 and ask the children to order these as they count in 5s.

Diagnostic Check marking key: First Mental Arithmetic 2

Below each set of answers you will find **Activity prompts** for helping children to overcome difficulties. Use these activities diagnostically so that you can assess when children understand the concept.

Counting

1   13   **2**   19

Activity prompt: Ask children to count out 15 counters. Then ask them to place them in any arrangement that they like and ask: *How many counters are there now?* Repeat this for different quantities. Now place between 11 and 20 counters in a random arrangement and ask them to count them. Repeat for other quantities.

Reading, writing and ordering numbers to 20

3   9   12   14   15   **4**   17   **5**   1 ten and 9 ones drawn

Activity prompt: Provide two sets of 'Numeral cards from 0 to 9', 'Two-spike abacus 1', and some counters. Ask children to use the counters to show 15 on the abacus and place the appropriate numeral card under each spike. Repeat this for other TU numbers until children are confident.

Addition and subtraction

6   15   **7**   2   **8**   4   **9**   9

Activity prompt: Write $6 + 3 = \blacksquare$ and ask children to 'read' this aloud. Now challenge them to explain how they would answer this. If they have no method, suggest that they start with the larger number and count on for three. Repeat this for subtraction, counting on from the smaller to the larger number. For word problems ask them to read the problem with you and to say which words give clues as to the type of problem.

1 and 10 more or less

10   1   **11**   18   **12**   10   **13**   40

Activity prompt: Begin with a simple example, such as: *What is 1 more/less than 5?* Repeat this for other examples, inviting children to explain each time how they found the answer. If they are unsure, use 'Number lines without the numbers' to model the questions. Repeat for teen numbers. Use a metre rule marked in decimetres and ask children to say the 10 more/less than numbers for 50, 70, 20, and so on.

Combining groups of 2, 5 and 10

14   8   **15**   10   **16**   40   **17**   30

Activity prompt: Provide number lines, such as 'Number lines from 0 to 20', and ask children to make 3 jumps of 2. Ask: *What number did you finish on? So 3 jumps of 2 is 6.* Repeat this for other numbers of jumps of 2, and then for jumps of 5. Use a metre rule marked in decimetres and repeat for jumps of 10.

Sharing into equal groups

18 5   **19** 2   **20** 1   **21** 4

Activity prompt: Provide 10 counters and 10 pieces of paper. Put down two pieces of paper and ask children to share the counters equally between the two pieces. Ask: *What is 10 shared by 2?* Repeat this for sharing by 5, then for sharing by 10. Then repeat for other quantities, such as 20 counters and share by 2 and by 5.

O'clock times

22 8 o'clock   **23**   **24** 3 hours

Activity prompt: Use a teaching clock face and show different 'o'clock' times. Ask children to say the time and to explain how they know that it shows that time. Then ask children to set the hands on the clock to the 'o'clock' times that you say.

Measures

25 Pencil with a tick is longer than the other pencil.

26 Cup with line for water at the top or near to the top.

Activity prompt: Ask children to compare the length of two items and to order them, shorter first. Repeat for three items. For capacity provide identical cups. Allow children to put some water into one of them, then to pour more/less into the other. Repeat for three containers. Provide a balance and ask children to compare two parcels, saying which is heavier/lighter, and how they know that.

Shapes

27 Drawings of a square, triangle, circle and rectangle under their names.

28 Three circles and two rectangles drawn.

Activity prompt: Provide some shape tiles and ask children to name them. Turn the shapes into different orientations on a flat surface and ask: *What shape is this? What if I turn it this way? What shape is it now?*

Position, direction and movement

29 Simple drawing of a chair with a book on top.

30 Refer back to question 29. There should be a ball drawn under the chair.

Activity prompt: Ask children to hold a book. Now say, for example: *Put the book on the table. Put it under the table. Put the book next to the table …*

Diagnostic Check marking key:
First Mental Arithmetic 3

Below each set of answers you will find **Activity prompts** for helping children to overcome difficulties. Use these activities diagnostically so that you can assess when children understand the concept.

Reading, writing and ordering numerals to 20

1   14 15 17   **2**   16

Activity prompt: Using 'Number lines from 0 to 20', repeat question 1. Ask children to say the numbers as they move their finger along the number line. Repeat for other missing numbers.

Writing numbers 1 and 10 more and 1 and 10 less

3 20   **4** 30

Activity prompt: Ask children to say the number that is 1 more or less than a given number. Begin with 6, for example, then move to teen numbers. Repeat this for 10 more/less than multiples of 10. If children falter, provide a number line, perhaps from 'Number lines from 0 to 20', for 1 more/less, and a metre rule marked in decimetres.

Addition

5 7   **6** £9

Activity prompt: Provide some quick recall practice for addition of small numbers. If children falter, remind them to start with the larger number and count on to find the total.

Subtraction

7 3   **8** 11

Activity prompt: Ask children to explain how they subtract 5 from 8. If necessary, teach the method of counting on from the smaller to the larger number. Provide further practice in the recall of subtraction of small numbers.

Doubles of numbers to 10

9 12   **10** 16

Activity prompt: Model the doubles with towers of interlocking cubes. Start with smaller numbers such as double 2 and double 3 and show that doubling these gives the same answer as adding: 2 + 2 = 4, and so on. Provide opportunities for children to recall these facts, for example during oral and mental starters.

Combining groups of 2, 5 and 10

11 20   **12** 12   **13** 40p   **14** 20p

Activity prompt: Provide a number line, such as from 'Number lines from 0 to 20', so that children can model combining. Ask children to start at zero and find where, say, 3 or 4 hops of 2 finish. Repeat this for hops of 5. Use a metre rule marked in decimetres to model hops of 10.

Sharing into equal groups

15 3   **16** 7   **17** 5

Activity prompt: Model the sharing by using counters. Ask children to count out, for example, 14 counters, and to share these equally into 2 sets. Ask: *How many counters are there in each set? So what is 14 shared by 2?* Repeat this for sharing into sets of 5, then of 10.

Halves and quarters

18 3   **19** 5   **20** 2

Activity prompt: Provide 8 counters. Ask children to find half of the counters. If necessary show them that the counters can be put into two groups of 4. Say: *Half of 8 is 4.* Now repeat this to find a quarter of 8. Check that children place the counters into four groups of 2. Repeat for other quantities, such as 12 and 16.

Symmetry

21 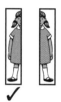 ✓   **22**

Activity prompt: Provide paper and scissors. Ask children to fold the paper in half, then draw a simple shape which is half of a picture, such as half of a butterfly. Point out where the fold is. They cut out the picture then open out the paper. Repeat this by folding and cutting other shapes.

Sorting diagrams

23

A multiple of 5	Not a multiple of 5
5 10 15 30	6 9 12 18

24

Has 4 sides	Does not have 4 sides

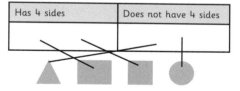

The numbers may be shown in any order.

Activity prompt: Draw a simple two-region Carroll diagram. Write 'Is a multiple of 2' in the left-hand side, and 'Is not a multiple of 2' in the right-hand side. Ask children to sort the numbers 1 to 10 onto the diagram. Discuss where each number fits and why.

Telling the time to o'clock and half hour

25   **26**   **27** 2 hours

Activity prompt: Provide a clock face with hands and ask children to show you the times that you say. Include both 'o'clock' and 'half past' times. Challenge children to explain how they know when it is an 'o'clock' time, and when a 'half past' time.

Position, direction and movement

28 Simple drawing of a chair with a cat on it.

29 Refer back to question 28. There should be a mouse drawn under the chair.

30 Drawing of something that turns such as a windmill sail, a door handle or clock hands.

Diagnostic Check marking key:
First Mental Arithmetic 4

Below each set of answers you will find **Activity prompts** for helping children to overcome difficulties.
Use these activities diagnostically so that you can assess when children understand the concept.

Reading, writing and ordering numbers

1 19 **2** 30 50

Activity prompt: Write a number as a word, such as fifteen, and ask: *What number is this? How would you write it using numbers?* Repeat for other teen numbers. Then challenge children to say what numbers are missing in sequences such as: 16, 18, 20, …, …; and 25, 20, 15, …, ….

Odd and even numbers

3 49 **4** Seventy-seven

Activity prompt: Ask children to write the numbers 1 to 10. Now ask them to point to the even numbers, then the odd numbers. If they are unsure, explain that every other number is even, starting from 1 (odd). Then tell them to write the numbers 11 to 20 under their first row of numbers, so that they see that it is the ones digit that determines whether a number is odd or even.

Using greater than (>) and less than (<) signs

5 46, 47, 48, 49, (50) **6** 66, 65, 64, 63, 62, 61, (60)

Activity prompt: Revise the meaning of < and > with children. Ask them to say number sentences aloud, for example, given 36 < 40, they say '36 is less than 40'. Repeat for 'greater than' sentences.

Adding three single-digit numbers

7 17 **8** 14 **9** 15

Activity prompt: Remind children to look for all pairs of numbers that add to 10 and to add those first. Provide some examples such as: 9 + 4 + 1; and 4 + 8 + 6.

Addition and subtraction

10 61 **11** 68 **12** 47p **13** 14p

Activity prompt: Ask, for example: *What is 58 add 3? How did you work that out?* If children are unsure, simplify this to 8 + 3, then add 50. Repeat for subtraction, asking, for example: *What is 52 subtract 3?* Simplify to 12 − 3, then ask children to calculate 52 − 3 using the same method.

Doubles and halves

14 8

15 8

16 9p

Activity prompt: Provide 'Number lines from 0 to 20' and ask children to use this to help them to find doubles. Say: *What is double 3?* They count on from 3 for a count of 3 to 6. Repeat for other doubles. Explain that if a double is known then a half can be found easily. For example, double 6 is 12, so half of 12 is 6.

Multiplication and division

17 18

18 40

19 7

20 7

Activity prompt: Provide 'Number lines from 0 to 20' and ask children to make jumps of 2 to find multiples of 2. For multiples of 5 and 10 use a metre rule marked in centimetres in the same way. Show children how to make jumps back to find divisions.

Halves, quarters and three-quarters

21 8

22 4

23 12

Activity prompt: Model the questions using squared paper. Ask children to find $\frac{1}{2}$, $\frac{1}{4}$ then $\frac{3}{4}$ of 16 squares. Repeat for other numbers such as 12, 20 and 24.

Reading scales

24 17cm

25

40cm   50cm

Activity prompt: Use a ruler marked in centimetres. Ask children to point to measurements that you say, such as: *18cm, 14cm*. Extend this to finding similar measurements using a metre rule marked in centimetres.

Telling the time

26

27

Activity prompt: Show a clock face and ask children to set the hands to the times that you say. Check that they understand what happens to the hour hand for 'quarter past', 'half past' and 'quarter to' times.

Shapes

28 Drawings of a triangle, rectangle and pentagon.

30 Drawing of a circle.

29
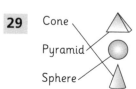
Cone
Pyramid
Sphere

Activity prompt: Ask children to sort some 2-D shape tiles and some 3-D models of regular shapes. Check they understand that 3-D shapes have 2-D faces, for example, a cuboid has rectangular faces.

Diagnostic Check marking key: First Mental Arithmetic 5

Below each set of answers you will find **Activity prompts** for helping children to overcome difficulties. Use these activities diagnostically so that you can assess when children understand the concept.

Reading and writing numbers to 1000 in digits and words

1 Four hundred and ninety-two

2 83 is the same as 8 tens and 3 ones

Activity prompt: Write a two-digit number using numerals and check that children can write this using words. Extend to three-digit numbers. Now provide a number written with words and ask children to write this with digits. Use 'Two-spike abacus 2' to check that children understand that, for example, 71 is the same number as 7 tens and 1 one.

Odd and even numbers

3

Is odd	Is not odd
37 49 75 81	10 36 82 94

The numbers may be shown in any order.

4 Odd

Activity prompt: Check that children understand that every other number, starting from zero, is even: 0, 2, 4, 6, … Ask children to make jumps of 2 starting from zero along 'Number lines from 0 to 20'. Compare, for example, 4 and 14; 8 and 18. Explain that it is the ones digit that determines whether a number is odd or even.

Doubles to 20

5 32

6 38

7 28p

Activity prompt: Check that children know the doubles of all numbers to 10. Then ask them to calculate the double for 11. Ask: *How did you do that?* Repeat this for the other doubles of numbers to 20. Provide practice at recall of these facts during an oral and mental session.

Addition and subtraction

8 4

9 11

10 8p

11 3p

Activity prompt: Ask children to explain how they made the calculations. If they are unsure, remind them that they can use 'counting on' methods for both addition and subtraction. Ask: *How would you calculate 47 add 4?*

Multiplication and division

12 45

14 9

16 30

13 10

15 14

Activity prompt: Ask children to give some answers to questions about multiplication or division by 2, such as: *What is 5 multiplied by 2? There are 16 sweets to be shared by 2 children. How many would they have each?* Repeat this for questions about 10, then about 5. Check that children understand that if they know, for example, 7 × 5 = 35, then they can deduce that 35 ÷ 5 = 7.

Halves, quarters, three-quarters and one-third of quantities and shapes

17 Any three-quarters shaded, e.g.

18 12

19 6

> **Activity prompt:** Provide squared paper. Ask children to draw a shape with 16 squares in it. Ask them to shade half. Then ask them to calculate what a quarter would be, then three-quarters. Repeat this for a shape with 20, then 24 squares.

Shape and space

20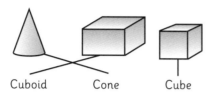

Cuboid   Cone   Cube

21 One line of symmetry drawn (five possible)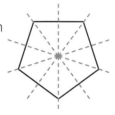

> **Activity prompt:** Review the names and properties of 3-D shapes. Ask children to examine some shape models and to say how many sides, and what shapes these are. Then ask children to draw around a pentagon shape tile, cut out the shape, then find different ways to fold it to find the possible lines of symmetry.

Reading scales

22 41 written on scale.

23 46 written on scale.

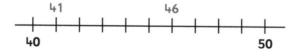

> **Activity prompt:** Use 'Number lines without the numbers'. Tell children to write 40 at a point on the line, count along to 50, and write 50 in its place. Now ask children to show where, for example, 49 would go, and so on.

Time

24

25

26 15 minutes

27 45 minutes

> **Activity prompt:** Show a clock face. Ask children to say the times that you show, such as five to one or ten past 11. If children are unsure, count around the clock face in 5s to remind them how many minutes past the hour or how many minutes to the next hour each time is.

Whole, half and quarter turns

28 Quarter turn

29 Half turn

30 Half turn

> **Activity prompt:** Tell children to face front, then turn to face, say, the table. Ask how far they have turned. Repeat this so that children make whole, half and quarter turns.

Diagnostic Check marking key:
First Mental Arithmetic 6

Below each set of answers you will find **Activity prompts** for helping children to overcome difficulties. Use these activities diagnostically so that you can assess when children understand the concept.

Read, write and order numbers

1   999

2

> **Activity prompt:** Ask questions such as: *What is the hundreds/tens/ones digit? How do you write that using digits?* Provide 'Number lines without the numbers' and tell children to mark, for example, 50 to 60. Then ask them to place 51, 59, and so on. Repeat for other decades.

Symbols < and >

3   >

4   <

> **Activity prompt:** Provide two copies of 'Two-spike abacus 1' and counters and ask children to model the question. They model 63 then 36 and compare the two. Ask: *Which is greater? So which is smaller?* They write the number sentence 63 > 36. Repeat for other pairs of two-digit numbers.

Addition and subtraction

5   97

6   2

7   82cm

8   15g

> **Activity prompt:** Ask children to explain the calculation methods that they are using. Remind them to use what they know, such as: 52 + 30 = 50 + 30 + 2 = 80 + 2 = 82. For subtraction or difference check that they count up from the smaller to the larger number.

Multiplication and division

9   16

10   20

11   6

12   8

13   5

> **Activity prompt:** Ask children some multiplication table questions such as 6 × 5, 10 × 10. Discuss how, if a multiplication fact is known, a division fact can be deduced, for example, 6 × 5 = 30 so 30 ÷ 5 = 6.

Pairs to total 20, pairs of multiples of 10 to total 100

14   9

15   70

> **Activity prompt:** For pairs of multiples of 10 to total 100, compare, for example, 6 + 4 = 10 and 60 + 40 = 100. Write these out one under the other. Repeat this for another example, and explain that what the children already know can be used to find another fact. For pairs to total 20, provide 'Number lines from 0 to 20' and ask children to use them to find pairs that total 20. They can write these out in a table: 1 + 19, 2 + 18, and so on.

Doubles of numbers to 20 and matching halves

16 15   **17** 34

Activity prompt: Model the doubles with two towers of interlocking cubes put together, then invite children to find half of the total by snapping the tall tower in two. Write the number sentence, such as: *Double 11 is 22; half of 22 is 11*. Discuss how, if children know the double, they can deduce the half.

Halves, quarters and three-quarters of numbers and shapes

18 8   **19** 12

Activity prompt: Use squared paper. Tell children to mark out a rectangle containing 20 squares. Ask them to shade a quarter and say how many squares that is. Repeat this for a half, then three-quarters.

Time

20 ten past seven   **21** five to four   **22** 30 minutes

Activity prompt: Model the questions using a teaching clock. Check that children understand where the hands are for quarter past and quarter to, and relate this to digital time.

Reading scales

23 6   **24** 17

Activity prompt: Use 'Number lines without the numbers', marked from 0 to 10, then 20, where each little mark represents one. Ask children to count along the number line, pointing to each number place. Now ask them to write in where 5, 15, 3, 8, 16 … are.

Shapes

25 Cone   **27** Sketch of a right-angled triangle

26 Cylinder   **28** Sketch of a circle

Activity prompt: Use shape tiles for 2-D shapes and 3-D models. Ask children to name the shapes and to give a property of each shape. Now challenge them to find a square face on one of the 3-D models. Repeat this for a rectangular face, then a circular face.

Right angles

29 6   **30** 1

Activity prompt: Begin with some shape tiles. Challenge children to find the right angles and to follow these with their finger. Provide some squared paper. Tell children to draw a shape with some right angles. Ask them to point out the right angles. Repeat for other drawn shapes.

Schofield & Sims First Mental Arithmetic

General Resources

Use these resources as the children begin working through the **First Mental Arithmetic** books.

Every resource in this section may be photocopied after purchase for use within your school or institution only.

The Language of Maths: Book 1

Add	+	more than, and, in total, altogether, plus
Subtract	−	take, less than, fewer than, take away, minus
Equals	=	makes, is

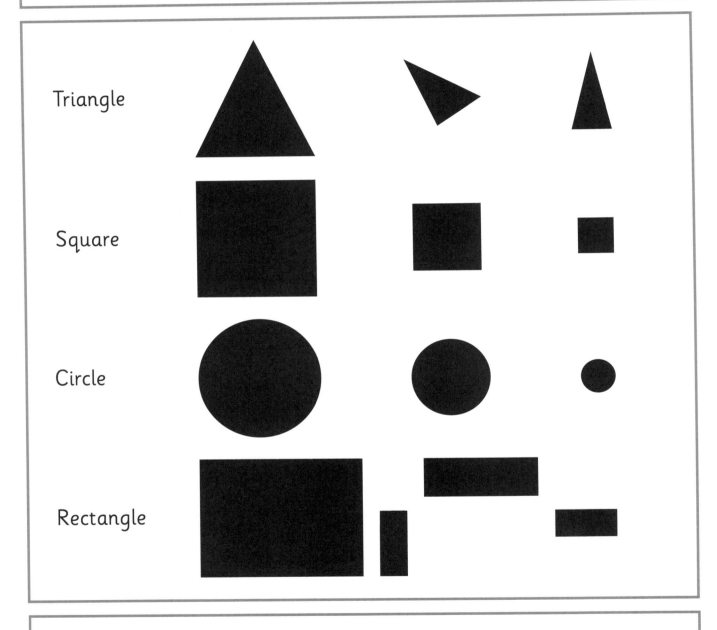

Triangle

Square

Circle

Rectangle

Longer

Shorter

Wider

Narrower

The Language of Maths: Book 2

Add	+	more than, and, in total, altogether, plus
Subtract	−	take, less than, fewer than, take away, minus
Equals	=	makes, is

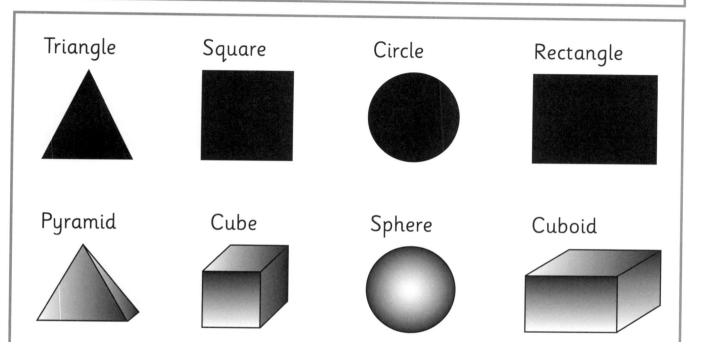

Triangle   Square   Circle   Rectangle

Pyramid   Cube   Sphere   Cuboid

Turn   Half turn   Quarter turn

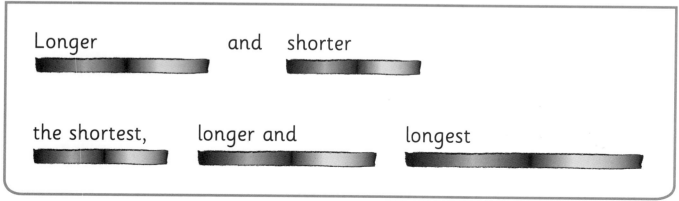

Longer   and   shorter

the shortest,   longer and   longest

The Language of Maths: Book 3

Add   +   more than, and, in total, altogether, plus

Subtract −   take, less than, fewer than, take away, minus

Equals   =   makes, is

$4 + 2 = 6$
$6 - 4 = 2$

Pyramid   Cube   Sphere   Cuboid

Turn   Half turn   Quarter turn

Measure

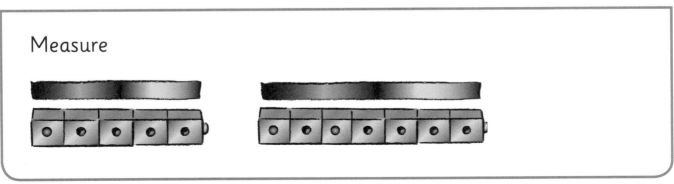

The Language of Maths: Book 4

Add	+	more than, and, in total, altogether, plus
Subtract	−	take, less than, fewer than, take away, minus, difference
Multiply	×	times, lots of, groups of, product
Divide	÷	share, divided by, shared between, group into
Equals	=	makes, is

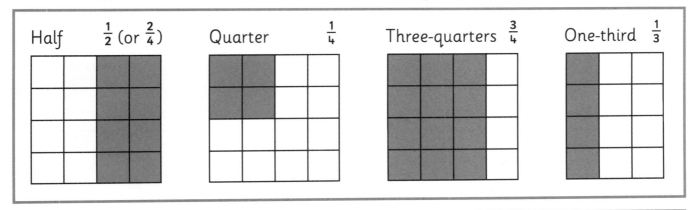

Half $\frac{1}{2}$ (or $\frac{2}{4}$) Quarter $\frac{1}{4}$ Three-quarters $\frac{3}{4}$ One-third $\frac{1}{3}$

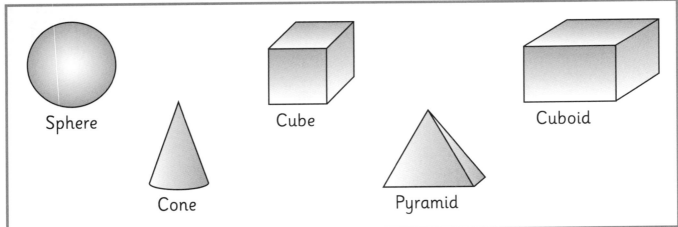

Sphere   Cube   Cuboid

Cone   Pyramid

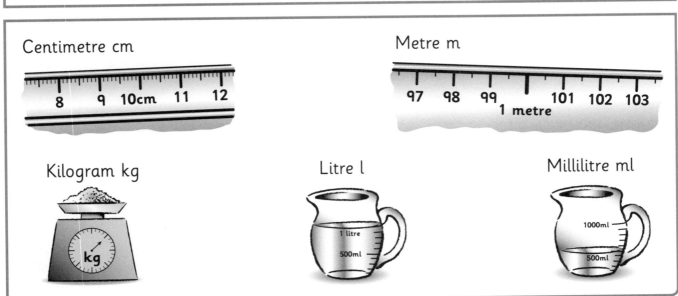

Centimetre cm   Metre m

8 9 10cm 11 12

97 98 99 1 metre 101 102 103

Kilogram kg   Litre l   Millilitre ml

kg

1 litre
500ml

1000ml
500ml

The Language of Maths: Book 5

Multiply	×	multiply, times, lots of, groups of, product
Divide	÷	divide, share, divided by, shared between, group into

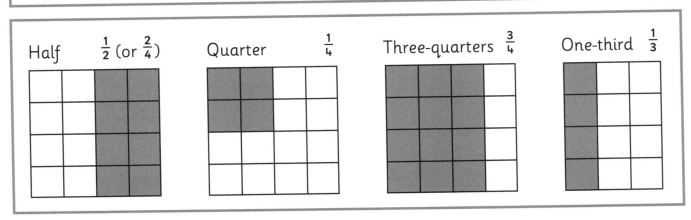

Half $\frac{1}{2}$ (or $\frac{2}{4}$)   Quarter $\frac{1}{4}$ Three-quarters $\frac{3}{4}$ One-third $\frac{1}{3}$

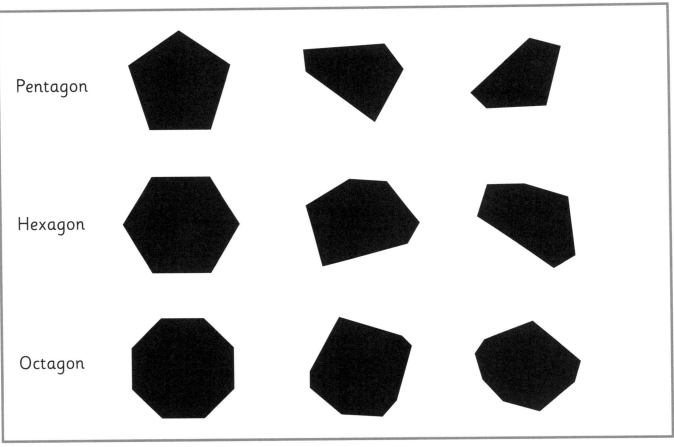

Pentagon

Hexagon

Octagon

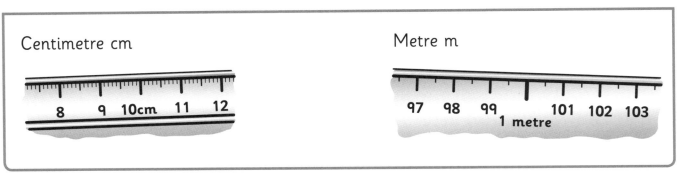

Centimetre cm

Metre m

1 metre

The Language of Maths: Book 6

| Multiply | × | multiply, times, lots of, groups of, product |
| Divide | ÷ | divide, share, divided by, shared between, group into |

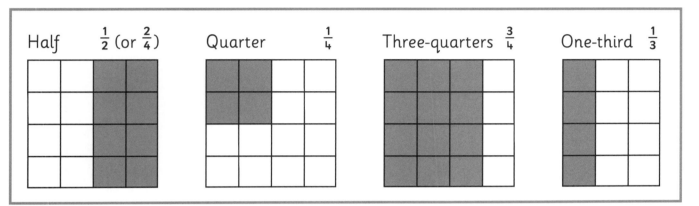

Half $\frac{1}{2}$ (or $\frac{2}{4}$)   Quarter $\frac{1}{4}$ Three-quarters $\frac{3}{4}$ One-third $\frac{1}{3}$

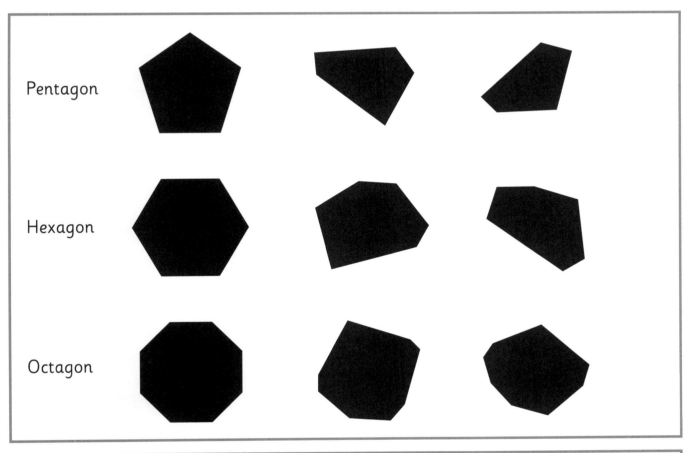

Pentagon

Hexagon

Octagon

Millilitre ml   Litre l   Gram g   Kilogram kg

Two-spike abacus 1

Use counters on the abacus to show the tens and ones.

Place numeral cards in the boxes under the abacus to show the number.

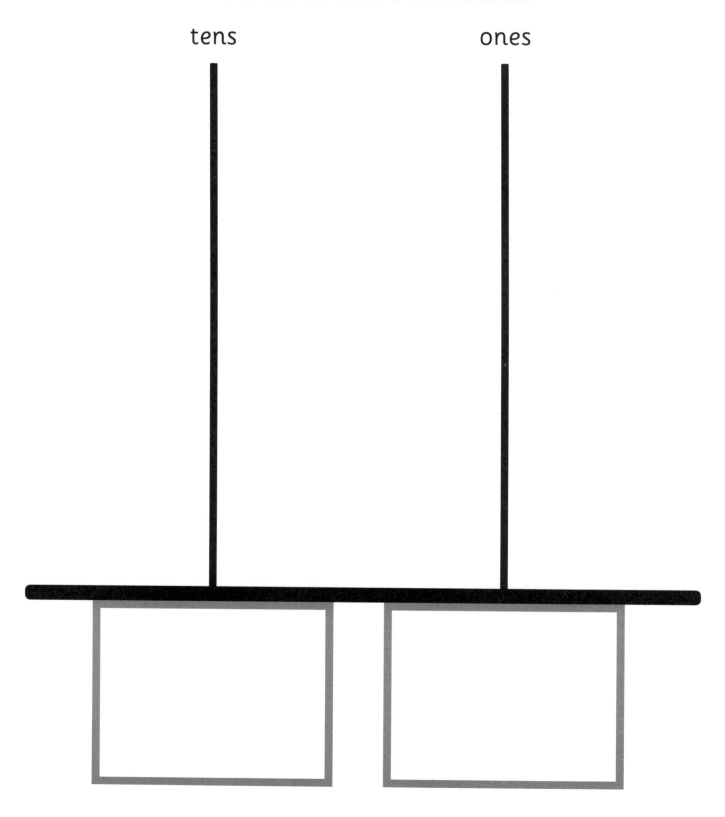

tens   ones

Two-spike abacus 2

Draw the beads to show the tens and ones.

Write how many tens and how many ones in the boxes.

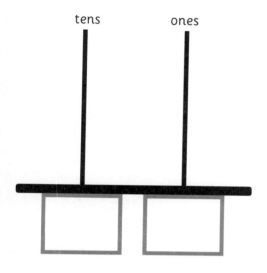

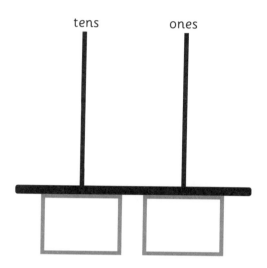

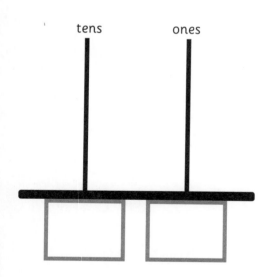

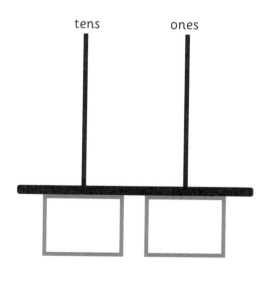

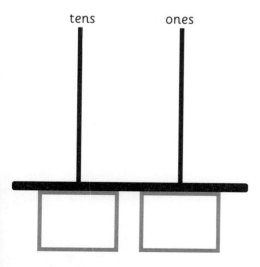

Numeral cards from 0 to 9

Photocopy onto card and cut out the cards.

0	1
2	3
4	5
6	7
8	9

Number lines from 0 to 20

Photocopy onto card and cut out each number line.

| 0 | 1 | 2 | 3 | 4 | 5 | 6 | 7 | 8 | 9 | 10 | 11 | 12 | 13 | 14 | 15 | 16 | 17 | 18 | 19 | 20 |

| 0 | 1 | 2 | 3 | 4 | 5 | 6 | 7 | 8 | 9 | 10 | 11 | 12 | 13 | 14 | 15 | 16 | 17 | 18 | 19 | 20 |

| 0 | 1 | 2 | 3 | 4 | 5 | 6 | 7 | 8 | 9 | 10 | 11 | 12 | 13 | 14 | 15 | 16 | 17 | 18 | 19 | 20 |

| 0 | 1 | 2 | 3 | 4 | 5 | 6 | 7 | 8 | 9 | 10 | 11 | 12 | 13 | 14 | 15 | 16 | 17 | 18 | 19 | 20 |

| 0 | 1 | 2 | 3 | 4 | 5 | 6 | 7 | 8 | 9 | 10 | 11 | 12 | 13 | 14 | 15 | 16 | 17 | 18 | 19 | 20 |

| 0 | 1 | 2 | 3 | 4 | 5 | 6 | 7 | 8 | 9 | 10 | 11 | 12 | 13 | 14 | 15 | 16 | 17 | 18 | 19 | 20 |

| 0 | 1 | 2 | 3 | 4 | 5 | 6 | 7 | 8 | 9 | 10 | 11 | 12 | 13 | 14 | 15 | 16 | 17 | 18 | 19 | 20 |

| 0 | 1 | 2 | 3 | 4 | 5 | 6 | 7 | 8 | 9 | 10 | 11 | 12 | 13 | 14 | 15 | 16 | 17 | 18 | 19 | 20 |

Number lines without the numbers

Photocopy onto card and cut out each number line.

Word cards with numbers as words from one to ten

Photocopy onto card and cut out the words.

one	two
three	four
five	six
seven	eight
nine	ten

Word cards with numbers as words from eleven to twenty

Photocopy onto card and cut out the words.

eleven	twelve
thirteen	fourteen
fifteen	sixteen
seventeen	eighteen
nineteen	twenty

Schofield & Sims First Mental Arithmetic

1 to 100 chart

Photocopy onto card.

1	2	3	4	5	6	7	8	9	10
11	12	13	14	15	16	17	18	19	20
21	22	23	24	25	26	27	28	29	30
31	32	33	34	35	36	37	38	39	40
41	42	43	44	45	46	47	48	49	50
51	52	53	54	55	56	57	58	59	60
61	62	63	64	65	66	67	68	69	70
71	72	73	74	75	76	77	78	79	80
81	82	83	84	85	86	87	88	89	90
91	92	93	94	95	96	97	98	99	100

Days of the week

Monday

Tuesday

Wednesday

Thursday

Friday

Saturday

Sunday

Conservation of number

1	one	●
2	two	●●
3	three	●●●
4	four	●●●●
5	five	●●●●●
6	six	●●●●●●
7	seven	●●●●●●●
8	eight	●●●●●●●●
9	nine	●●●●●●●●●
10	ten	●●●●●●●●●●

Full list of Schofield & Sims First Mental Arithmetic books

Pupil books

First Mental Arithmetic 1	ISBN 978 07217 1163 8
First Mental Arithmetic 2	ISBN 978 07217 1164 5
First Mental Arithmetic 3	ISBN 978 07217 1165 2
First Mental Arithmetic 4	ISBN 978 07217 1166 9
First Mental Arithmetic 5	ISBN 978 07217 1167 6
First Mental Arithmetic 6	ISBN 978 07217 1168 3

Answer books

First Mental Arithmetic 1 Answers	ISBN 978 07217 1169 0
First Mental Arithmetic 2 Answers	ISBN 978 07217 1170 6
First Mental Arithmetic 3 Answers	ISBN 978 07217 1171 3
First Mental Arithmetic 4 Answers	ISBN 978 07217 1172 0
First Mental Arithmetic 5 Answers	ISBN 978 07217 1173 7
First Mental Arithmetic 6 Answers	ISBN 978 07217 1174 4

Teacher's Guide

First Mental Arithmetic Teacher's Guide	ISBN 978 07217 1210 9

Free downloads

A range of free downloads are available from the Schofield & Sims website (www.schofieldandsims.co.uk).
These downloads may be used to support pupils in their learning, both in school and at home.
They include the following items:

- two **First Mental Arithmetic** Entry Tests to help you choose the best book for each individual

- an Achievement Award certificate for each **First Mental Arithmetic** book

- Maths Facts downloads to provide a quick reference tool

- a National Curriculum Chart to show how each book supports the programmes of study.